This Book
Belongs
to

Wendy Walker

Tell me about
God's Plan for Me

By MARY ALICE JONES

Illustrated by
DOROTHY GRIDER

 RAND McNALLY & COMPANY

CHICAGO   NEW YORK   SAN FRANCISCO

Bible references (in order of reference)

Psalms 8:3–6a
John 1:12;
Galatians 3:26; 4:6
Deuteronomy 6:17–18
Psalms 19:8–14
Proverbs 16:32
Proverbs 16:7
Isaiah 1:16c, 17
Amos 5:24

Matthew 5:43–46
Matthew 5:1–11
John 10:10
John 13:35
Matthew 7:12
Galatians 6:10
Luke 10:25–37
Hebrews 13:8
Deuteronomy 33:27

I Peter 5:7
Psalms 23
Matthew 6:25–33
Matthew 22:36–40
Romans 8:28
I Corinthians 9:24–25
I Corinthians 12:4–27
John 14: 1,3; 16:22
I Corinthians 15:35–44; 51–54

Contents

Who Am I?

THE car was all packed. Bobby and his daddy and his mother and his little sister, Mary, were going on a trip. Mother and Mary were to stop at Grandmother's for a visit, and Bobby and Daddy were going on to Washington.

They reached Grandmother's house in time for lunch. After lunch Bobby and Daddy said good-bye for a few days.

Bobby had never been to Washington. He and his daddy had made a list of things he wanted to see. "I can't wait to see the space ship," Bobby said as they drove along.

So as soon as they reached Washington they went to the Smithsonian Institution. The first American space ship to go around the earth had been put there so that people might see it.

There it was! It looked so little to have gone so far! Then there was a movie showing the astronaut and telling how he had orbited the earth.

After they left the museum, Bobby and Daddy sat on a bench in the grounds to rest. "It was exciting, Daddy," Bobby said.

7

"But I wondered. How did they know the space ship would go round the earth and come back? It could get lost way out in space."

"They didn't *know*, Bobby. But they had learned the natural laws. They knew they could depend on them. And so they could plan ways to use the laws. They worked it all out very carefully."

Bobby looked back at the museum. "But how could the men learn all these laws? And make a space ship go around and come back? It seems too much to learn."

"It does seem almost too much to learn, son. But way back in the beginning, God had a purpose. He planned for man to be able to learn the laws God made, and to know how to use them."

"Tell me about it."

"The very first chapter of the Bible tells us that 'In the beginning God created the heavens and the earth'—and plants and fish and birds and animals. Then God planned for man to be. Man was to be a creature different from all the rest on earth. For man was to be able to love God and to work with God. He was to be able to learn to understand God's plans for creation."

Bobby nodded slowly. "But it is so much to understand."

"Yes, it is, Bobby. As we think about the vast universe and then think about man, he seems so small."

"He is," Bobby said. "Man is very small compared with the Milky Way and the sun and all the space that goes on and on."

"There are some Bible verses which seem to say just what we are thinking," Daddy continued. And he repeated the verses:

"When I look at thy heavens, the work of thy fingers,
The moon and the stars which thou hast established;
What is man that thou art mindful of him,
And the son of man that thou dost care for him?
Yet thou has made him a little less than God,
And didst crown him with glory and honor.
Thou hast given him dominion over the works of thy hands."

Bobby listened. "That says God thought man is important."

"More important than anything else in creation," Daddy agreed. "And these verses say something else, too."

"What else do they say?"

"That God trusted man to work with him in his creation. 'Thou hast given him dominion over the works of thy hands.' "

Bobby thought about it. "Why did God plan for man to be more important than stars and mountains and everything?"

"We do not know all about God's plans, Bobby. But we do know that God planned for man to be a creature who could love and think and plan and imagine."

Bobby thought some more. "It is important to be able to love and to think. Yes, it is very important."

"The Bible says it this way, son. God called his human

creatures to be sons of God. Not just things, but *persons,* persons who can love God as Father and come to understand and respond to God's good purposes for him."

"I am glad God planned so much for us," Bobby said. "I am glad I am a person."

"And you are a good person, Bobby."

"Am I, Daddy?" Then Bobby looked anxious. "Does God want me to learn all his laws about all the universe?"

Daddy roughed his hair and chuckled. "Well, maybe not *all* of them at once. But you are making a good beginning."

Why Am I Here?

BOBBY and John had been swimming in the community swimming pool. Now they were sunning themselves by the side of the pool. It was quiet there. Some people were having a snack in the refreshment center.

"Where do you suppose Susan is?" Bobby wondered lazily. John lived on one side of Bobby, and Susan and her toddler brother, Jack, lived on the other side. "Her mother said they were coming."

"Maybe Jack didn't wake up, or something," John replied.

Bobby and John felt too drowsy to talk any more.

Then all of a sudden they heard a splash. Not a splash like a swimmer diving, but a little splash. They jumped up.

"It's Jack!" Bobby yelled, as he saw the curly head go under the water. Quick as a flash Bobby and John were in the pool, and in a minute they had Jack safe on the side, crying loudly.

"There, Jack, you're all right," Bobby said. "But where did you come from? We didn't see you." He looked toward the refreshment center. Susan and her mother were running. "He's all right," Bobby called. "He was in the shallow part. We got him out."

Susan's mother hugged Jack close. "We stopped to talk to a new neighbor. Jack was with us. Then suddenly he was gone."

"I didn't see him go," Susan said. She looked about to cry.

"He's not hurt, Susan," Bobby told her. "He's just frightened. Come on, Jack. Don't cry."

The little boy peeped from his mother's shoulder. Bobby winked at him, and Jack scrambled out of his mother's arms.

Jack's mother turned toward the boys. "Thank you, Bobby and John. It is so good you were here at this very minute when Jack needed you." She looked at Jack. "He is such a little boy. It could have been serious."

That night Bobby's mother and daddy told him they were proud of him and John for keeping their heads and acting quickly.

"It wasn't serious, but it might have been," Daddy concluded.

"That's what Susan's mother said, Daddy. She said it was good we were right there that minute. It made me wonder."

Bobby's daddy looked at him questioningly.

"I wondered if God planned it that way. Planned for us to be there, I mean. When Jack needed us."

His daddy put his arm around Bobby. "Jack did need you and you were there," he said. "But it isn't like magic, Bobby. We think God doesn't just pick people up and put them down in time to prevent an accident. Accidents do happen."

Bobby seemed puzzled. "You said that people are important to God. Was God counting on us to help Jack?"

"God counts on you always to work with him, to show love to other people in whatever way they need you. That is why you are in the world, son. To be what God planned for you to be, his loving, helping child."

"All the time," Mother added. She smiled at him. "Not just when you can rescue a little boy from a pool. Sometimes it is harder when it is just ordinary and everyday."

Bobby grinned as he remembered what had happened after lunch. "Like not yelling under Mary's window when she is asleep?"

Mother was serious again. "Nobody else in all the world can be what God plans for you to be."

Bobby thought it over. "I think I know what you mean, Mother. I am here, always to be what God wants me to be."

Then he laughed. "Not just when I hear a splash!"

Can I Know What Is Right?

BOBBY and John and Susan and their dogs, Rover and Samson and Ginger, were playing in Bobby's yard. All of a sudden, Samson growled angrily. He dashed to the sidewalk and began fighting a big Persian cat that had just moved in down the street.

John raced after Samson and caught his collar.

"Why, Samson, whatever made you do that?" John scolded. "You *know* you are not supposed to chase cats."

"You mean, he *should* have known it. But he didn't," Susan declared. "He did chase the cat."

"That doesn't mean he didn't know better," John insisted.

Bobby's mother had heard the excitement and came out to see what it was about. They told her what had happened. "Samson was being bad. He was doing what he knew he shouldn't do," John said. "I'm going to shut him up in his house." So John marched off with a subdued Samson at his heels.

"Do dogs really know what is right and what is wrong, Mother?" Bobby asked.

Mother sat in the yard chair. "That is a hard question to answer, Bobby."

"People are supposed to know. Are dogs, too?"

"Not in the same way, I think."

Susan sat on the ground. "But Samson and Rover and Ginger are smart," she said. "They know a lot."

"Yes, they are smart dogs and they do know a lot, Susan. But I believe not in the same way as people know it."

"Why isn't it the same way?" Bobby wanted to know.

Mary, Bobby's little sister, ran out from the house. She had a jumping jack in her hand. "Look! The boy wiggles when I make him," she said as she pushed back and forth on the frame.

Mother made room for her in the chair. She took the jumping jack in her own hand. "This jumping jack can't do *anything* except what you make him do. He is a puppet. He is not alive."

"But that isn't like a dog," Susan protested.

"No, it isn't, dear. Rover and Samson and Ginger are alive. They can run and eat and catch a ball and learn to do many things. And they grow rather like people do."

"Then why are they different from people about knowing what is right and wrong?" Bobby asked.

"What I think they know, Bobby, is what you and John and Susan like and what you don't like."

"How do you mean?"

Mother gave the jumping jack back to Mary. "When your dogs were very young, you taught them to run and to sit down when you told them," she explained. "You liked it when they did what you told them to do. You patted them and told them they were nice dogs. They liked your voice when you said that."

"And when they didn't do what we told them to do," Susan added, "we scolded them. And they didn't like our voices." She

twisted around to pat Ginger. "That is the way it still is. They do what we want them to do. That is, most of the time they do."

"Mother, do you mean that dogs can't think for themselves and decide like people can? Is that what the difference is?"

"Something like that, I think, Bobby. We don't know all about it. Some dogs seem to love people as well as obey them."

Susan stroked Ginger's head. "I think Ginger loves me."

Mother nodded. "But I think people are *special*. I think God planned for people to love and think and understand in special ways. Ways that even smart dogs can't know."

"And people can make choices for themselves," Bobby broke in. "Daddy says God doesn't *make* us do what is right."

"But didn't Samson choose to chase the cat?" Susan asked.

"Not in the same way, I think, that John chose to make

Samson let the cat go. John *understood* why it was bad for his dog to attack a neighbor's cat. He knew it hurt the cat and hurt the neighbor's feelings, too. And he knows that to have dogs and cats fighting would make an unfriendly street."

"Samson just ran out and jumped on the cat without thinking. He can run and fight but he can't understand when he should *not* fight. Is that the way it is?" Bobby inquired.

"I think it is something like that."

"Well, sometimes I do that, too," Bobby admitted. "Sometimes I start something without thinking what will happen."

"People do that sometimes, Bobby," Mother agreed.

"But people really know better," Susan said, "when they are big like us. They can think and decide what is right because they know God's plan for loving each other. They have learned what hurts people and what is friendly and kind."

"My jumping jack doesn't hurt people," Mary announced.

Mother touched the doll. "No, dear, your jumping jack can't do anything at all. *You* do it."

She turned to Bobby and Susan. "What makes it so sad when a *person* does something that hurts someone else, is that most of the time we could know a better way to do."

Bobby nodded. "If we used the special gifts of thinking and making choices that God planned for people."

Does It Matter What I Do?

BOBBY and his mother and daddy and Mary were watching television in their living room. There had been a big parade with bands and flags and the President and great crowds of people.

"That was exciting, with the President and the crowds and the bands and everything," Bobby said, when it was over.

Mary skipped about. "I liked the children waving flags."

Daddy turned off the television. "Yes, that was a fine parade."

"I guess the President of the United States is the most important man in the world, isn't he?" Bobby asked.

"The man we elect President has a very important job, son."

Mother turned up the light. "In our own country and all around the world," she added.

Bobby was thinking. "Daddy, I know it matters what the President does. But I am not important like that. Does it really make any difference what *I* do?"

Mary looked surprised. "Why, Bobby, you know it matters if you forget to feed Rover! He gets hungry!"

"Oh, *that!* That's not anything," Bobby responded.

He turned to his daddy. "I don't see how the things I can do can make much difference. I can't stop wars or get schools for children or anything like that."

"Can't you, Bobby? Are you sure about it?"

"Why, Daddy, you know I can't. How can I?"

"Of course you can't by yourself, Bobby." Daddy pointed to the television. "But not even the President can do these big things by himself. You and Mother and Daddy and Mary and our neighbors and all the other good citizens have to help him."

"But—I just don't understand that." Bobby went to his mother's chair. "Do you understand it, Mother? How I can make a difference about war and schools and important things?"

"It isn't easy to see just how it is, dear. But big things usually begin with little things. And you and each one of us can make a difference in many little things."

"How can what I do help us not to have wars?"

Mother thought a minute. "I just remembered a wise old saying I read a few days ago. It says,

> He who is slow to anger is better than the mighty,
> And he who rules his spirit than he who takes a city."

Bobby looked as if he found this hard to believe. "How can my not acting angry be that important?"

Daddy picked up the Bible. "Here is another wise saying:

> When a man's ways please the Lord
>   he makes even his enemies to be at peace with him."

"Does it mean that if I don't act mean with people and try to do what God wants me to do, it will make a difference in what happens in our country and the world?"

"I think it does, Bobby. I think the way you feel toward other people and the way you act really does make a difference."

"But what about what the other people do? The ones who don't like us? I can't make *all* the difference, can I?"

Mother shook her head. "We can't say that if you try not to act angry and to do what you think God wants us to do there will never be any more trouble among people."

Bobby sighed. "I thought it couldn't be that way."

Mother went on. "There are many, many persons in the world, you know. When one person does what God wants him to do, he cannot be sure that nothing evil will ever come to pass. There is hatred and evil in the world."

"Then does it count? What I do, I mean?"

Daddy answered, "Yes, son, we think God planned it this way. The world is God's place of working. He depends on each one who loves him to be the sort of person who can do the good things he wants done. So each one is important to God. The sort of person you choose to be makes a difference to you, to your country, to the world, and to God."

Mary climbed into her daddy's lap. "Well, I think it makes a difference if Bobby remembers to feed Rover, don't you, Daddy?"

"That I do, darling! Little things count, too. You help Bobby not to forget Rover!"

Why Should I?

BOBBY and John were on their way home from school.

"Why did our room vote for that old puppet show?" John grumbled. "They should have *known* our idea was better."

Bobby kicked a stone. "They must have gone crazy."

Their room had been discussing what they would do for their part in the school festival celebrating important events in the story of their state. Bobby and John had wanted to have a play telling about the time the first railroad came through. They had read about it in a library book. But the plan that won the most votes was for a puppet show about the first settlers.

When Bobby reached home, he threw his books on the table.

"Is something wrong, dear?" his mother asked.

"Yes, there is. I think the people in our room are dumb."

"What has the room done that you don't like?"

So Bobby told his mother about the discussion of the part in the festival and the vote for the puppet show.

"It is not a good idea, Mother. Puppet shows are hard to

make right and the early settlers didn't do anything exciting."
Bobby pounded the table. "The railroad coming through *was*
exciting."

"Did you tell the room about the idea for the railroad show?
And why you thought it would be good?" Mother asked.

"We did, Mother. John and I had the library book with
pictures. They should have listened. It would have been good."

"Yes, it probably would have been good," his mother agreed.

"Well, I'm not going to work on any old puppet show."

"Aren't you, son?"

"Let the silly people who voted for it work for it. John and
I will read in the library while they are doing it." And Bobby
looked as if he thought that settled it.

"I know you are cross about the way the room voted, son.
But the room did vote that way, you know, and you had a vote."

Bobby spoke slowly. "Yes, I voted." Then he burst out angrily. "But I don't want to work on a puppet show! Why should I?"

"That is an important question, Bobby. People often ask, 'Why should I?'"

"Do they? Well, why should I work on the puppet show?"

"Are you sure you don't know the answer, Bobby?"

Bobby was quiet for a moment. "You mean because we all voted? I should do what the vote said?"

"That is part of the answer. Not all of it, I think."

"What is the rest of the answer, Mother?"

"You and Daddy and I were talking about how God planned for his human creatures to love him and work with him."

"Yes, but how is it working with God to make silly puppets?"

"That isn't quite the way it is, is it, son?"

Bobby sighed. "No, it isn't. Tell me how it is."

"God calls all of us to work with him for a good world. An important part in having a good world is for us to learn how to get along with people. It is important to respect each other as persons and respect each other's ideas, so everybody can grow and be his best self."

"Is that why I should work on the puppets? Because God wants me to help our room get along together? And not hurt people's feelings by making fun of ideas I don't like?"

"That is the way I think it is, son."

"I wasn't nice about the puppets," Bobby admitted. "But, Mother, do you *honestly* think the puppet show is a good idea?"

Mother laughed. "Well, you haven't told me much about the puppet show idea, have you?"

Bobby laughed, too. "You know what I think. I think you *know* puppets are hard. I think you know our idea was better. But you are going to help us take the old puppet idea and work at it so it will be the best part of the whole school festival."

How Can I Be Happy?

MARY and Susan and her little brother, Jack, were having a tea party at Susan's house.

"Let's pretend I'm a fairy," Mary said.

Susan finished her sandwich. "All right, Mary. How will you pretend you are a fairy?"

"I will fly around with wings." So Mary ran on tiptoe around the porch waving her arms. Jack did not know what Mary was doing but he ran after her, waving his arms and laughing.

Bobby and John came around the corner of the house.

John pointed toward Susan's porch. "What are they doing?"

Bobby shrugged. "Playing some pretend-game of Mary's."

"They look silly," John said.

Bobby agreed. "But maybe they think it's fun."

Bobby's mother called just then to tell Bobby his favorite television program was about to begin, so the boys watched.

"That was good," John said, as the program ended.

Bobby turned off the television. "It's fun to watch good

programs." Then he remembered seeing Susan and Mary and Jack on Susan's porch. "Lots more fun than playing babyish pretend games."

He turned to his mother. "What makes something fun?"

"Why, Bobby, I think something is fun when you enjoy doing it, when you feel jolly and like laughing as you do it."

"Is it playing? Instead of working?"

"Usually we think of *playing* as fun and *working* as something we do because we are responsible for doing it," Mother explained. "But some people seem to *like* working, even more than playing."

"Well, I don't," John announced. "I think it's fun to play ball but it isn't fun to do homework."

"Sometimes it isn't fun," Bobby agreed. "But last night when Daddy and I found places on the globe, I liked it. It was what I had to do, but we laughed and had a good time."

John was remembering. "Well, sometimes it *is* fun. Like when the librarian helped us find out about the railroad."

"Is having fun the same as being happy, Mother?"

Mother thought a minute. "I think there is a difference, Bobby. Having fun is usually something gay we do for a while and finish, like playing a game."

"If we played ball all the time we would get tired of it," Bobby agreed. "Then what is being happy, Mother?"

"I think being happy is having a joyous feeling inside us that stays with us all the time."

"Inside us? What do you mean, Mother?"

"I think it is rather like what the Bible calls blessed."

"What is blessed?" Bobby asked.

"It seems to mean happy in God's sight," Mother said.

"I don't understand that," John told her.

"I think being really happy, John, is being what God planned for us to be as his children. Not just doing what other people think is fun or will succeed."

"Can't I be what God wants me to be and have fun, too?" Bobby asked anxiously.

Mother looked at his solemn face. She laughed. "Why, son, being blessed isn't being gloomy and sad and dull!"

"Then tell me what it is."

"I think it is what Jesus meant when he said he wanted people to 'have life to the full.'"

"How do people have life to the full?" John wanted to know.

"I think by loving God and loving people and understanding them. People who live this way aren't afraid. They aren't tied up tight inside. They *enjoy* doing what they know God wants them to do. And so they are happy and good companions."

"People like that would be nice to know," Bobby said.

"They are, son." Mother smiled. "And they have fun, too!"

Why Do I Do What Is Wrong?

YOU have spoiled everything!" a boy shouted angrily.

Bobby and John were in the craft room at their school. That morning their room had been invited to see the model airplane the older boys had been working on. They had liked it. So at recess Bobby and John had gone back by themselves to see it again.

"You know you are not supposed to handle our work," the older boy stormed. "Now look what you have done!"

What they had done was to try to make the wings work as they had seen the older boys do in the demonstration. But they did not know how, and so had broken the wings loose.

Now as they saw the broken wings and the angry sixth-grade boy, Bobby and John were frightened.

Some other boys came into the craft room. They were all furious. "It will take us a week to fix it!" one of them yelled. "And we wanted to exhibit it in the craft fair next week."

Bobby and John knew they couldn't fix the plane. "We're sorry," Bobby said. "We didn't mean to spoil the wings."

33

"'Didn't mean to,'" one of the boys mimicked. "You know the rule about not touching another grade's work, don't you?"

Bobby and John nodded. They knew the rule.

Just then the bell rang for the end of recess and all the boys went back to their own rooms.

That night after dinner Bobby and his daddy talked about what had happened. Bobby was unhappy. "It was such a *good* model, Daddy. I know they would have won a blue ribbon at the fair for it. And now they can't, because we spoiled it."

"Yes, you did, son."

Bobby was quiet for a while. "We knew we shouldn't do it," he said. "We knew the rule about the craft shop."

"You told me about it and we agreed it was a good rule," Daddy remembered, "not to bother another group's work."

"We did it just because we wanted to work the wings."

"That usually is why we do things we shouldn't, Bobby.

We seem to think we may do whatever we want to do."

"But we can't, can we? Because of other people. Like the boys not being able to exhibit their plane when we broke it."

"It seems that something like that often happens, son."

"But, Daddy, *why* do we do what we know we shouldn't?"

"We don't have to, you know."

"But we *do*. You said God planned us to be his children. Why didn't he make us so we would be better?"

"We can be what God planned for us to be, Bobby. But we have to want to."

"I want to be, but I don't. Why don't I?"

"I think it is because you and I want to be God's children. But at the same time, we want to do whatever we want to do without thinking about God's plan for us or other people."

Bobby thought it over. "When we want to do something very much, we just forget about wanting to be God's children."

Daddy listened. Bobby went on. "But it doesn't turn out very well when we do, does it?" He sighed. "I wish God had a bell he would ring to remind us when we are about to forget."

Daddy put his arm around Bobby. "All of us need reminding. What we want to do seems so very important to us."

"Yes, it does. I *wanted* to work those airplane wings. I didn't think about anything else."

"But God does remind us, Bobby. In all the ways he shows us how much he loves us, he is reminding us all the time that we are his children. And that we can be happy when we remember to act like it."

"I want to remember. Let's ask God to help me remember."

So Daddy and Bobby asked God to help them remember all the time that they are God's children and to act like it.

How Can I Help Other People?

IT WAS a cold, foggy day. Bobby and John and Susan were at Bobby's house. His daddy had said they could use his workroom to make Thanksgiving decorations for their room at school.

Bobby was putting some gold paint on a cluster of magnolia leaves John's mother had given them. He stood for a moment holding the paintbrush.

"These decorations look pretty," he said. "But couldn't we do something more important for Thanksgiving?"

Susan finished a mat she had been making of corn husks.

"But, Bobby, a pretty room makes us all feel good."

John was working on a festoon of evergreens. He turned to Bobby. "What do you think we should be doing?"

Bobby himself looked rather puzzled. "I'm not sure I know," he admitted. "But I was thinking about people who need things. Food and a warm place to be on a cold day, and things like that."

Bobby's mother came in with some popcorn. While they ate popcorn, Bobby repeated his question.

37

Mother touched the gay decorations. "The decorations cheer people up on a gloomy day like this. And that helps people."

"I think so, too," Susan said.

"But, Susan, if you and I were really hungry, would pretty decorations be what would help us most?" Mother added.

"That is what I was thinking about," Bobby said. "How can we help people who need something important?"

"It isn't just our deciding that we will do something to help somebody, Bobby. We try first to understand how *they* feel."

"But, Mother, how can we know how somebody else feels?"

"We can't always be sure, son. But we can try to imagine."

John draped his festoon over a peg. "Imagine? How?"

"Imagine how I would feel and what would help me if things were turned around. If I were the other person and he were I."

Bobby chuckled. "That sounds funny. 'If I were the other person and he were I.'"

Mother agreed. "But it is hard to think that way. To put yourself in some other person's place and understand how he feels."

"Tell us some more about it," John asked.

Mother sat down. "How does the Golden Rule say it?"

Bobby and John and Susan remembered. They repeated, "Whatever you wish that men would do to you, do so to them."

Mother smiled at them. "It's easy to say, isn't it?"

"I know what you mean when you say that, Mother! You mean it is *not* easy to *do*."

John spoke slowly. "Putting myself in somebody's place first," he began as if thinking it out. "And then doing what I would want somebody else to do for me in that place."

"Then if we want to help people we have to know about them, don't we?" Bobby asked. "We can't just decide what *we* think."

Susan picked up the magnolia leaves Bobby had gilded. "I think people need different kinds of help. Sometimes something pretty is what they need. Like this."

"And sometimes the help they need is somebody to like them and invite them to play ball," Bobby said. He looked at John. "I think Lem, that new boy at our school today, was lonesome."

John nodded. "We didn't imagine how we would feel if we were in a new school and didn't know anybody."

"I am putting myself in the place of Mrs. Hunter down the street," Susan announced. "Our mothers have taken food to her all the time she has been sick. And people have sent flowers. But in her place I would be tired of everything. I would want something *different*. Like gilded magnolia leaves."

They all laughed. "I think you have done a good job of imagining, Susan," Bobby's mother said.

"I'm putting myself in Lem's place," Bobby went on. "I'm going to call him and tell him I'll show him around school."

So Bobby called up Lem. Susan gilded some leaves for Mrs. Hunter. Then it was time for Susan and John to go home.

Bobby sat by his mother. "There are some people who are cold, right in this town," he said. "Our teacher at church told us. If I were in their place, I would want somebody to find me."

"It would be very important that someone find you, Bobby."

"But how can I help them?" Bobby wanted to know.

"You *are* helping, Bobby. In several ways."

Bobby looked surprised. "What have I done to help?"

Mother went to a closet and took out a suitcase.

"You remember how these clothes kept you warm? Then you and I saw that they were all mended and clean? Daddy is taking them tonight to another boy who needs them to keep warm."

Bobby looked at a sweater and some wool shorts and some shirts and a coat. "Those things are too little for me. I don't need them. I'm not helping much by sending them."

"It isn't just sending your clothes that helps, Bobby. You help by being *you*. Because Daddy and Mother see that you need warm clothes, you remind us that other boys need them,

too. Because Daddy and I love you and Mary, you remind us that other children need love, too."

Bobby looked rather doubtful. Mother gave him a hug. "Do you remember what Jesus said about loving others, too?"

"You mean, 'Love your neighbors as you love yourselves?' And his story to show 'neighbor' means anyone who needs us?"

Bobby paused. "Does that mean I should want that boy to have warm clothes as much as I want them for myself?"

"What do you think it means, dear?"

"If I put myself in his place, what would I want? I guess that is the way I should decide it."

"And if you care about another boy as you care about yourself you would want him to know that someone like Daddy loves him."

Bobby thought it all over. "I think I need to learn more about it," he said. "Helping people as I would want them to help me takes a lot of understanding."

Mother nodded. "It does indeed, Bobby." She moved away. "And now, if I put myself in Daddy's place and do for him what he wants done for him, I will begin getting dinner ready."

Bobby jumped up. "And I will clean up his workroom!"

How Do I Know When To Change?

BOBBY and Mary were at Grandmother's. They were looking at a big album of family pictures taken a long time ago.

Bobby pointed to a picture of some women. "Look, Mary, aren't their dresses funny?"

Mary looked at the long, full skirts and tight waists. "Why did they wear dresses like that?"

"Because they wanted to, I suppose. But ladies now have changed the styles."

Grandmother came over to look at the book with them. She smiled at the pictures.

"I don't think these dresses are pretty," Mary said.

"Don't you, dear? I can remember when we thought they were very pretty. Our idea of what is a pretty dress seems to change."

Bobby found a picture of an old automobile.

"I think they needed to get a new car," Mary said.

Grandmother looked. "Oh, Mary, that *was* a new car! A neighbor took the picture because our new car was so beautiful!"

"Cars change, too," Bobby explained to Mary. "People learn how to make them better all the time, don't they, Grandmother?"

"Yes, Bobby. Changes have made cars better than they were when I was young." She looked toward the utility room. "And just look at that washing machine! And that refrigerator. When I moved into this house we couldn't get such things."

Mary looked puzzled. "But, Grandmother, why couldn't you get a washing machine?"

"Because nobody knew how to make one, Mary. Now they do. And so we have a better way to wash clothes."

"It's that way about everything, isn't it, Grandmother?"

"About many things, Bobby. Look at our farm, with all the new machines and the new fertilizers. Those changes are all good."

"And men have learned about the ocean and the weather and about exploring space, too. Daddy says my books are different from his when he was a boy. They have changed because men have learned more about the universe."

"And they will go on changing, because men will go on learning more and more." Grandmother thought a moment. "But there are some things that do not change, Bobby."

"Why, I thought we were learning more about *everything!*"

"I hope we are learning more about everything, dear. But some things we are learning to *understand* better, rather than to change."

"What are the things we don't change?"

"We don't change God, Bobby. But we do grow in our understanding," Grandmother went on. "We are trying all the time to understand better what God is like and how to worship him and what he says to us in the Bible and what he plans for us to be and do."

"Tell me more about it, Grandmother."

"In the very beginning God planned a good world for us and planned for us to be his children, to love him and trust him and worship him and work with him."

Bobby nodded. "That is what Daddy told me."

"And God helped men to know how to understand the world and how to live together happily. All through the years he has been showing us the way to have a good life."

"You mean like the Ten Commandments and the Golden Rule and loving your neighbor as much as you love yourself?"

"These are summaries of God's plan that have not changed."

"Inventions and explorations change things around us, but God's plan for us doesn't change? Is that it?" Bobby asked.

"I think that is the way it is, dear. But we have had to learn more and more about what God's plan means. The way people live changes. We have to learn new ways of loving our neighbor and new ways of expressing our worship of God."

"What are some of the new ways?"

"Before people had automobiles, they didn't need much control of traffic. Now, it is very dangerous not to obey traffic rules. So a new way of loving our neighbor as God has always wanted us to do, is to obey traffic rules."

Mary sat on Grandmother's lap. "It wouldn't be loving our neighbor if we ran through a red light, would it?" she said. "We might hurt somebody."

Bobby closed the album. "And we learn that some nations have different ideas from ours. Airplanes make them close neighbors now. We must understand them instead of fighting them."

Grandmother continued. "And as we learn more about God's plans for his children, we understand better how to pray. All the people it includes when we say, 'Our Father.' And all the new ways of showing love it calls for when we say, 'Thy will be done.'"

Bobby put the album in the bookcase. "Well, it looks like there is a lot of learning to do even about plans that don't change."

He thought a minute. "But, you know, Grandmother, I am glad some things don't change. Like God and his plans for us. It's good we can depend upon them always. And grow in understanding them."

Does God Care About Me?

MARY had gone with her mother to a weekday meeting at their church. Mary had stayed with the children in their room.

After the meeting was over, Mother came by Mary's room to tell her to wait there while she went for the car. She had had to park around the corner because the street in front of the church and the entrance to their parking lot was being repaved.

Mary stood at the window watching the big road machines at work. Soon Mother came, and she and Mary drove home. Mary was so quiet that Mother asked, "Did you have a pleasant time, dear?"

"Yes, we did. But I was wondering about the big machines."

"The road machines, Mary? What were you wondering?"

"They are so big. They could smash me flat."

"They certainly could, dear."

"I don't like it," Mary said.

"But we need machines," Mother told her. "It would be hard for men to dig up the street and flatten it out again. And it would take a long time. Isn't that something good to think about?"

Mary nodded. She asked, "But does God care about me?"

"Do machines make you think God doesn't care about you?"

"They could smash people. Why couldn't God get the work all done without those big machines?"

"I think God doesn't just suddenly decide on big road machines and put them to work, dear."

Mother slowed up to make a turn. "Men used the minds God has given them and the laws God has made. They learned to make machines to get important work done more easily and more quickly."

"I'd rather we didn't have them," Mary insisted.

"Would you, dear? People often feel unhappy about machines. They feel that machines make people less important."

"That's what I mean, Mother. Less important to God."

Mother thought a while. "Machines can do much more work than men can do, Mary. People often feel frightened when

they think about how powerful they are." She gave Mary a pat. "But machines can't work by themselves, you know."

Mary looked up. "Can't machines work by themselves?"

"Sometimes they do what men did not expect. But this is because men make mistakes in operating the machines. Machines can not plan; they do what men decide they are to do."

"Then the people are more important than the machines?"

"I think there is no doubt about it, Mary. Because only people can think and love God and learn about his plans."

"Then God does care about me? He doesn't want the machines to hurt me?"

"I am sure of it, dear. And I am sure he wants Mother and Daddy and all the people who manage our city and all the men who operate the machines to help him take care of you."

Mary thought some more. "I have to help take care of myself too, don't I, Mother?"

"Yes, you do, Mary. In our country where there are so many big machines, unless you help by remembering and obeying the safety signals, it would be very hard to take care of you."

"Even for God?"

"You see, dear, God expects you to use the gifts he has given you of being able to think and understand."

Mary nodded as Mother waited for a green light.

"You know, Mother, maybe letting me think and understand is one of the best ways God shows he cares about me more than about big machines." She nodded her head. "Yes, I know it is."

Why Do People Suffer?

BOBBY rushed into his house and called to his mother.

"Mother, Roy has been taken to the hospital."

"I am so sorry, Bobby. Do you know what is the matter?"

"Yes; he has pneumonia. Is that a very bad sickness?"

"Pneumonia isn't anything to take lightly, Bobby."

Bobby hung up his raincoat. "Roy won't die, will he?"

"We certainly think he will get well, son. Thanks to new medicines, most people who have pneumonia now do get well."

Bobby followed his mother into the kitchen. "Do you get pneumonia from being wet and cold?" he asked.

"Getting wet and staying cold sometimes seem to cause upsets that become pneumonia. Had Roy been wet and cold?"

"John said he had. John said Roy had done what his mother told him not to do, too. He had tried to jump over the creek, and he didn't make it. He should have known it is too wide."

"He fell in the creek and didn't go home to change clothes?"

"He didn't fall *all* in," Bobby explained. "But he got wet."

"I am sure staying wet on a cold day didn't help any, son."

"I have been wondering, Mother. Some of the boys said they thought God was punishing Roy for disobeying his mother."

"What do you think about it, Bobby?"

"I think it doesn't sound like God. But I know God expects us to use our minds and to listen to our mothers."

"And," Mother reminded him, "God planned laws for our bodies, like needing food and warmth and rest. Not to remember them causes us trouble."

Bobby was thoughtful. "God wants us to obey his laws because he loves us, and so we can be well and happy. Isn't that right, Mother?"

"That is what is most important to remember, I think."

Bobby came back to his question, "I still don't know whether God was punishing Roy or not."

"Let's see what we know about Roy," Mother suggested.

Bobby counted off the facts. "Roy didn't use his mind. He tried to jump across a creek that he could know was too wide for him. And he disobeyed his mother. And he got wet and cold. And he didn't change his clothes. And then he had pneumonia."

"All this we know for sure," Mother agreed.

Bobby went on. "And we think what Roy did was foolish and wrong, and that it made him get pneumonia."

"That is what we *think* about it," Mother pointed out. "But we cannot *say* that every time a boy disobeys or fails to use his mind he will get hurt or sick. Life isn't like that."

Bobby was remembering. "Like when our room was going through the factory and I left the group to see something and got into a dangerous part. A man found me and I didn't get hurt. But I had disobeyed the rules for the trip."

Mother went on. "And sometimes a person gets hurt or sick when he has used his mind and has not disobeyed the rules."

"When John broke his arm it wasn't his fault. He was careful. The sidewalk was icy and slick and he fell." Bobby went on. "And I remember the TV pictures of that flood when so many people got hurt. They couldn't help it when the dam broke."

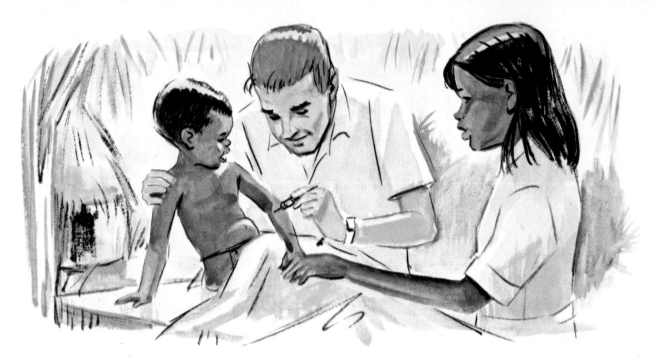

Mother nodded. "And sometimes people get hurt when they are helping other people. Like the doctor in Africa we read about who took the disease he was trying to find a way to cure."

"Then how can being sick and suffering be God punishing people?" Bobby asked. "He wouldn't punish people who weren't doing anything wrong or people who were helping other people."

"All through the years people have asked, 'Why do people suffer?'" Bobby's mother told him.

"Why does God make it so hard for people to understand?"

"I think God does not make it hard, Bobby. He does not hide the truth from his children. He helps them to understand."

"Then why don't we?" Bobby persisted.

"There is much to understand, son. God's plans are great plans. People are learning all the time. Boys and girls will go on learning after their mothers and daddies are old and tired."

"I would like to understand it all now," Bobby persisted.

Mother opened the oven to look at the roast. "Suffering seems to be a part of being a person, Bobby. It seems to help persons to understand themselves and each other. And to understand God's love."

"How does it, Mother?"

"I can't tell you all about it, dear. But there are two thoughts you can remember."

"What are they?"

"One is that God himself understands all about it. And God is great and good beyond our knowing."

"That is a big thought," Bobby said. "What is the other?"

"The other is that God loves you always. Suffering is not outside God's concern. Whatever happens, God cares about you."

Bobby looked at his mother. "Does God care about Roy's pneumonia even if it was his own fault that he got it?"

"I am sure God cares about Roy whatever he did. And wants to help him in whatever way he needs help."

"I am glad he does. I guess Roy is feeling pretty bad. He needs to know God cares about him." Bobby thought a minute. "But I do wish I understood all about it."

"I know you do, Bobby. And I want you to go on trying to understand all you can about God's love for persons."

What Are Things For?

BOBBY and John and Susan were coming home from a picnic. All of a sudden they heard a siren. An ambulance raced by and stopped in front of a new house that was being built down the street. Some men dressed in white quickly lifted out a stretcher and some strange-looking implements, and hurried into the house.

In a few minutes one of the men ran out again and dashed next door, calling back, "I'll phone the hospital for the new equipment."

Soon a car with a police escort screamed to a stop. Men hurried another strange-looking instrument into the new house.

Bobby and John and Susan waited where they were. After a while a neighbor came out and told them what had happened. A workman had fallen from a ladder and had been badly hurt. "The doctors from the hospital emergency room have been working hard," he said. "The new equipment helped."

"Did the doctors say the man will be all right?" Bobby asked.

"They said the equipment enabled them to save his life."

That night Bobby's daddy reported the man out of danger.

"Daddy, did they tell you about those new gadgets they had?"

"Yes, they are new inventions the hospital had been testing. They made a big difference in what the doctors could do."

"It was good they had those things they needed," Bobby said.

"This is a time when *things* were very important to a *person*," Daddy agreed. "Men had invented things that were good."

"Aren't things always important to persons?" Bobby wanted to know. "I think lots of things are important to me."

"Do you, son? Some things are important to you. Like warm clothes and a roof to keep the rain out and a bed to sleep in."

"But I like more things than that," Bobby said. "I like my record player and my bike and lots of things."

"They are fun to have, Bobby. And I am glad you have them. But only a few things are really important for a person."

"People want more than a *few* things," Bobby insisted.

"Yes, most of us like to have many things."

Bobby looked puzzled. "Daddy, you sound like things are bad to have. I think things are good to have."

"Sometimes they are. But I think we can make things bad for us instead of good for us."

"I don't understand what you mean, Daddy."

"It is easy for us to want things so much that we want more and more of them. We want them so much that we forget about wanting to be friends. Our *wants* get mixed up."

"You mean when we want things too much we make them too important? So other wants get left out? Like wanting to be good neighbors?"

Daddy nodded. "When we want more and more things, we want more and more money to get newer and finer ones. Then we use more and more of our time taking care of them. And we don't remember that we want to be good persons."

"We got a new car," Bobby reminded Daddy. "Wasn't that good?"

"Our old car was not running right any more. It was a thing that was not being useful to persons," Daddy explained.

Bobby frowned. "But our car isn't as big as Mrs. Miller's."

Daddy laughed and drew Bobby down beside him on the couch. "You see what I mean, son. Now you are thinking about a new car to show off in; not a car to meet our needs."

Bobby laughed, too. "I'd like to drive down the street in the very biggest car there is, to make everybody look."

Then his face was serious. "Is that how things are bad, Daddy? When we use them to show off with?"

"Something like that, son. Just think what would happen to our street if John's family wanted to get a car that was bigger than ours, and then Susan's family wanted a car that was bigger than John's, and then we wanted another new car bigger still!"

"You mean we would always be thinking about getting ahead of people? Using things to make us feel more important than our neighbors? And not caring about each other's feelings?"

"That is the way it seems to me, son."

Bobby thought it over. "But we use things when we need them, don't we? Like the doctors' equipment and our car?"

Daddy nodded. "Jesus told his friends that God knows his children need food and clothes and other things. 'Be not anxious,' he said. 'Think first about God and his good purposes.' Then Jesus promised, 'All these things will be yours as well.'"

"I like that," Bobby said. "Things are added on when we need them because God cares about us and wants us to have them. But loving God and loving people comes first."

"I hope we both remember that," Daddy said.

How Am I Different?

BOBBY'S class had gone to the public library to watch an artist at work. He had a sheet of paper on an easel. With crayons or a paintbrush he made pictures the boys and girls asked for.

"An Indian!" one boy called out. And the artist painted an Indian, dressed for a festival dance.

"A horse!" a girl asked. And the artist drew a horse with mane and tail flying. The boys and girls laughed and clapped.

After dinner that evening, Bobby and his daddy were in the workroom mending a chair that had a wobbly leg. As they worked, Bobby told Daddy about the artist at the library. "He made a picture of anything we asked. And each one was good."

"He must be a skillful artist to make so many pictures."

"I wish I could draw," Bobby complained. "I can't draw anything. My pictures are just about the worst ones in our room."

Daddy smiled. "Well, drawing is not what you do best."

"Why can't I draw good pictures, Daddy? I try hard."

Daddy tapped a tack into the chair. "Some people draw

pictures better than they do arithmetic, son. And some figure out how to orbit the earth better than they play the violin."

"But why, Daddy? Why can't I do *everything* if I try?"

"Most of us can do many things pretty well if we try," Daddy told him. "In fact, most of us have to learn to do many things." He chuckled. "Like your daddy mending a chair."

"I just *can't* draw a picture," Bobby insisted. "I *never* do one good enough to show at parents' day, like John and Susan do."

"People are different, Bobby. That is just the way it is."

"Did God plan it that way? That I couldn't draw pictures?"

Daddy laughed. "It isn't quite like that. I think God didn't just decide, 'Now I will plan for Bobby not to be able to draw.' "

Bobby laughed, too. "No, that isn't right. But how is it?"

"We do not understand all about it, son." Bobby held the tack box. His daddy went on. "We do know it is true that no two persons in all the world are alike."

Bobby wondered about it. "Among the millions and millions of persons in the world, is each one different from all the rest?"

"Each one is his own self, son. There is only one you."

Bobby wondered some more. "Did God think up all those different plans for persons?" he asked.

"It seems to be true, Bobby, that each one of us has a place all his own in God's great purposes."

"Does it mean that God has a special job for each one of us?

"I think it is not just one job for any one person, son."

"Then how is it?" Bobby persisted.

"I think God expects us to use all our mind and imagination and skill. But he doesn't expect each one of us to do everything equally well. He understands us. He knows we are different."

"Then I oughtn't to be mad because I can't draw good pictures like John and Susan can?"

"You ought not be unhappy about it. Do the best you can,

and just admit that John and Susan draw better than you do."

Bobby looked at his daddy and said emphatically, "But I do better in arithmetic. Our teacher said I understand it."

"You do seem to understand it very well, Bobby, and that is good. So you see how it seems to be. People are different."

Bobby watched his daddy test the chair. "People are different in more important ways than drawing and arithmetic," he said.

"What ways are you thinking of, son?"

"Some people are friendly, like you and Mother. And some of them are mean, like the man at Mr. Cliffe's farm who beat the horses. God didn't plan that way of being different, did he?"

"I think God's plan for each one of us is *good*," Daddy said.

"Then why are some people mean?"

"Nobody knows all the reasons, son. But some persons have never had anyone to teach them about God's plan. Some do not understand even when they are taught. And some seem not to want to understand."

Bobby was thinking hard. "But people themselves make the differences in being good, don't they? It's not like drawing, is it?"

"We can't say it quite that way, I think. Sometimes a person who seems to be bad, really wants to be good. He may even try harder than someone else who seems to be very good."

"But if he wants to be good, why doesn't God help him?"

"God does help him, son. And God loves him. But it seems true that it is harder for some people than it is for others to love people and to know how to be friendly and honest."

Bobby sighed. "It doesn't seem fair, that some people should do things better. And even be good without trying so hard."

"And some people learn easily and some cannot learn even

when they try," Daddy added. "Yes, it is difficult to understand."

Daddy had finished the chair leg. He sat in the chair to be sure it didn't wobble. Then he drew Bobby toward him. "Differences in people sometimes are puzzling," he said. "But think how interesting they are! Wouldn't it be dull if everybody looked alike?"

"Why, Daddy, they couldn't!"

"Of course they couldn't! And neither can they be alike in other ways. Some differences do seem unfair to some people. We do not understand all about it. But we know we couldn't have a good world of people without differences. Lots of differences. And we all need each other, with all our differences."

What Will Happen to Me When I Die?

SUSAN and Bobby were at John's house. His mother was helping them learn a new song. After a while she said, "You sing like angels!" This seemed funny to them. They teased each other.

That night after Mary had gone to bed, Bobby and his mother and daddy were sitting by the fireplace. Mother was knitting a sweater and daddy was reading and Bobby was looking at a new book about birds. Everybody had been quiet for a while.

"What will I be like after I die?" Bobby asked.

Daddy looked up. "What are you wondering about, son?"

"John's mother said we sang like angels. She was just playing." He pointed to his bird book. "But I thought about it again when I saw these wings. Will I be an angel when I die?"

"Would you like to be an angel, dear?" Mother asked.

"Well, I don't know much about them. But I think I wouldn't like it as much as being a boy."

"None of us knows much about angels," Daddy said. "But we do know God planned for us to be persons."

"Then I won't be an angel when I die?"

"Well, I think not like the pictures of angels you have seen. With a body rather like ours except for the wings."

"Then what will I be like, Daddy?"

"No one knows, Bobby. We can't even imagine."

"I would rather go on having this body," Bobby said.

"You know this body, son. You can do things with it. You help people with it. You have fun with it. It is the kind of body you need for this life. But after death there will be a new life, a different kind of life. You won't need this body then."

"But I like this kind of life. Maybe I won't like another one. Why doesn't God let me just go on having this body and living this life for always?"

Mother laid aside her knitting. "We hope you will go on having this body and living this life for a long time, Bobby. God wants you to do and learn and enjoy many things here."

"When John's grandmother died, you said everybody dies."

Mother nodded. "Yes, Bobby, everybody does die." She thought a minute. "Your life and everybody's life begins here in this world we know and goes on here for a while. After death, life changes. All of it is your life. But we do not know what your life after death will be like."

"I would rather know. Why does God keep it a secret?"

Daddy picked up the Bible. "Not exactly a secret, Bobby. Let me read something the Bible says." He found the place. "Jesus' friends were troubled because he had told them he soon would die. He said to them: 'Let not your hearts be troubled; believe in God, believe also in me. . . . Where I am you may be also . . . I will see you again and your hearts will rejoice.' "

"Did Jesus mean they would be with him after death?"

"I think so, son. He was telling his friends the most important thought about life after death. It will be a life where persons will be with God and know him and know each other."

"Will we work and help each other and have fun together?"

"We do not know, Bobby. What we do will be whatever will enable us to be happy with God and with each other."

"Will we understand the things we don't understand now?"

"I am sure we will understand God's plans much better than we understand them now. And we will be what God plans for us to be."

"But why don't we be what God plans for us to be now?" Bobby asked. "Why do we have to wait until after we die?"

Daddy lifted a log in the fireplace with the poker. "That is a very important question, Bobby. We cannot yet understand all that we want to understand or be all that we know God wants

us to be. But we can do much better than we are doing. Right now in this life we know, with these bodies we understand."

"That is what we ought to do," Bobby declared. "Then we wouldn't have to worry about what will happen after we die."

"No, dear, we would not have to worry about it," Mother agreed. "If we love God and love each other we begin eternal life now. So when we come to the new life after death we will feel at home, at home with God and with each other."

"I like that, Mother. Is that the way life after death will be? Not strange and frightening? But feeling at home?"

"I think life will be better than we had dreamed it could be, Bobby. I think this is the way God planned it. That his children may be at home with their Father forever."